OFFICIAL
PAST
PAPERS
WITH ANSWERS

INTERMEDIATE 2

ENGLISH
2006-2010

2006 EXAM – page 3
Close Reading
Critical Essay

2007 EXAM – page 13
Close Reading
Critical Essay

2008 EXAM – page 23
Close Reading
Critical Essay

2009 EXAM – page 33
Close Reading
Critical Essay

2010 EXAM – page 43
Close Reading
Critical Essay

SQA

BrightRED
PUBLISHING

First exam published in 2006.
Published by Bright Red Publishing Ltd, 6 Stafford Street, Edinburgh EH3 7AU
tel: 0131 220 5804 fax: 0131 220 6710 info@brightredpublishing.co.uk www.brightredpublishing.co.uk

ISBN 978-1-84948-120-5

A CIP Catalogue record for this book is available from the British Library.

Bright Red Publishing is grateful to the copyright holders, as credited on the final page of the book, for permission to use their material.
Every effort has been made to trace the copyright holders and to obtain their permission for the use of copyright material.
Bright Red Publishing will be happy to receive information allowing us to rectify any error or omission in future editions.

[BLANK PAGE]

X115/201

NATIONAL
QUALIFICATIONS
2006

FRIDAY, 12 MAY
1.00 PM – 2.00 PM

ENGLISH
INTERMEDIATE 2
Close Reading

Answer all questions.

30 marks are allocated to this paper.

Read the passage carefully and then answer **all** the questions, **using your own words as far as possible**.

The questions will ask you to show that:

> you understand the main ideas and important details in the passage—in other words, **what** the writer has said (**Understanding—U**);

> you can identify, using appropriate terms, the techniques the writer has used to get across these ideas—in other words, **how** he has said it (**Analysis—A**);

> you can, using appropriate evidence, comment on how effective the writer has been—in other words, **how well** he has said it (**Evaluation—E**).

A code letter (U, A, E) is used alongside each question to identify its purpose for you. The number of marks attached to each question will give some indication of the length of answer required.

SCOTTISH
QUALIFICATIONS
AUTHORITY

©

Women and chocolate: Simply made for each other

Women and chocolate are a dream team and advertisers have cleverly ensured they stay that way.

You can bet that when the first Aztec tentatively crushed a cacao bean, right behind him was an ad executive excitedly branding the muddy brown discovery "the food of the gods". Or if there wasn't, there certainly should have been—because chocolate hasn't looked back since. Mars' new "Mars Delight" is just the latest attempt to beguile us into
5 seeing that a mixture of fat, sugar and a type of caffeine is an essential part of our life.

The secret of chocolate's particular appeal lies in the cocoa butter—it melts just below body temperature—which gives it that delicious dissolve-in-the-mouth feeling. Add to that the sudden charge of energy you get from the sugar, the kick of the caffeine and another chemical, which acts as a mood enhancer—and you can understand why the
10 Aztecs originally decreed that only nobles, priests and warriors were allowed to eat it. Then it was seen as the cure for all ills. And it's true—as the confectionery industry is keen to point out—that cocoa beans contain flavonoids which help high blood pressure. And chocolate doesn't have the teeth-rotting qualities of other sweets.

But that's more than counterbalanced by the fact that it's still crammed full of fats and
15 sugar. "We are looking at 9 to 10 calories per gram," says Professor Tom Sanders, the head of nutritional sciences at King's College, London. "And while people admit to eating 18 grams of chocolate a day, the manufacturers think it's nearer 35 grams, about the size of a Crunchie bar. What's also worrying is the trend to "super-size" that we also see in the fast food industry that means that people end up consuming more. Of
20 particular concern is that chocolate bars contain vegetable fats—also known as trans fatty acids (TFAs)—which have been linked to coronary heart disease." Last summer both Nestlé and Cadbury said they were thinking of removing TFAs from their products.

"The Government recommends that less than 2 per cent of dietary energy comes from trans fats," says Hannah Theobald, nutrition scientist at the British Nutrition
25 Foundation. "It is good news that the food industry is looking at ways to reduce them in food products."

Ironically, these concerns are far removed from chocolate's beginnings—when, being made by teetotal Quakers, it was originally promoted here as a healthy alternative to alcohol. One of the first recorded advertisements was a couple of lines in the
30 Birmingham Gazette of March 1, 1824, placed by a John Cadbury. It read: "John Cadbury is desirous of introducing to particular notice 'Cocoa Nibs' prepared by himself, an article affording a most nutritious beverage for breakfast".

The nutritious link was one that early chocolate marketing followed. During the Second World War, manufacturers Caley's urged that female air raid wardens should be bought
35 a box of their Fortune chocolates not just because they'd enjoy them but because it would supply the "extra nutrition to keep them going". Early Mars advertising informed women that there was a "whole meal" in a bar to "nourish, energise and sustain".

"Women are the key to chocolate advertising," says Rita Clifton, the chair of the leading
40 branding agency Interbrand. "They are not only important consumers in their own right but they also act as gatekeepers to the rest of the family. So it's important to get the approach right." So as women's role in society changed so did the chocolate bars and advertising. Out went the stoic "meal on the run" idea, in came the post-Sixties "Me" sense of indulgence—running through fields or sitting in a bath eating a flaky chocolate
45 bar. "One of the most 'indulgent' adverts is the Flake one," Clifton says. "This is the

ultimate example of taking time out for yourself. OK, I could never quite see the point of eating a Flake in the bath—not very practical, but then fantasies aren't meant to be."

But experts say that in recent years the style has changed again. The Milk Tray man was kicked out in favour of the slogan "love with a lighter touch". The fashion,
50 according to Yusuf Chuku, a communications analyst at Naked Communications, is very much towards a lighter, more sophisticated approach. "Because of concerns about advertising to children, I think there's been even more of a move towards targeting women," Chuku says. "With health advice constantly changing, I think advertising is now less about the guilty secret idea, but saying it's OK to eat some chocolate as long as
55 you balance it with other things."

That's reflected in the different types of chocolate being developed—low calorie bars like Flyte, "lighter" bars than the monolithic-looking Mars or Snickers, or developments like Kit Kat Kubes, which can be shared among friends. It also explains the increased demand for organic or more exotic chocolates: if women are going to indulge, they want
60 to make sure it is with a high quality brand. Chuku says that in a competitive market worth £5 billion a year in the UK, no manufacturer can afford to miss which way the wind is blowing: "I think the next trend will be turning back to comforting chocolates you remember from your childhood. Watch out for the Wagon Wheel."

Glenda Cooper, in *The Times Body and Soul* (slightly adapted)

QUESTIONS

Marks   *Code*

1. Explain what is meant by the idea that chocolate "hasn't looked back" (lines 3–4) since it was discovered.   **1**   **U/A**

2. Identify and briefly explain any example of humour from the first paragraph.   **2**   **A**

3. Explain **in your own words** two of the reasons why chocolate has its "particular appeal". (line 6)   **2**   **U**

4. Explain why "But that's more than counterbalanced" (line 14) is an appropriate or effective link between the paragraph it begins and the previous one.   **2**   **A/E**

5. Explain **in your own words** the **two** concerns of Professor Tom Sanders (line 15) about people's chocolate consumption.   **2**   **U**

6. Why is it "good news" (line 25) that manufacturers are considering reducing the amount of fatty acids in their products?   **1**   **U**

7. Explain fully why "Ironically" (line 27) is an appropriate choice of word at this point in the passage.   **3**   **A/E**

8. (a) Look at the advertisement placed by John Cadbury (lines 30–32). Comment on the **word choice** or **tone**.   **1**   **A**

    (b) "The nutritious link was one that early chocolate marketing followed." (line 33)

      Write down an expression from the rest of this paragraph, apart from "nutrition" or "nourish", which continues the idea of nourishment.   **1**   **U**

9. Explain how effective "gatekeepers" (line 41) is as an image or metaphor.   **2**   **E**

10. (a) How does the writer's **word choice** in the sentence beginning "Out went" (line 43) make clear to the reader the changing role of women in society?   **2**   **U/A**

     (b) How does the **structure** of this sentence reinforce this idea of change?   **2**   **A**

11. Explain fully why the word "fantasies" (line 47) is appropriate to describe the ideas behind the Flake advertisement.   **2**   **A**

12. Look at the expression "kicked out". (line 49)

    Suggest **two** things this implies about the way people in the advertising industry conduct their business.   **2**   **U/A**

13. There are "different types of chocolate being developed". (line 56)

    Explain **in your own words two** ways in which these new products would help consumers to think that "it's OK to eat some chocolate". (line 54)   **2**   **U**

14. "Watch out for the Wagon Wheel." (line 63)

    (a) What can you deduce about what the Wagon Wheel was?   **1**   **U**

    (b) Give **two** reasons why this sentence might be an effective advertising slogan.   **2**   **A/E**

Total (30)

[END OF QUESTION PAPER]

X115/202

NATIONAL
QUALIFICATIONS
2006

FRIDAY, 12 MAY
2.20 PM – 3.50 PM

ENGLISH
INTERMEDIATE 2
Critical Essay

Answer **two** questions.

Each question must be taken from a different section.

Each question is worth 25 marks.

SCOTTISH
QUALIFICATIONS
AUTHORITY

Answer TWO questions from this paper.

Each question must be chosen from a different Section (A–E). You are not allowed to choose two questions from the same Section.

In all Sections you may use Scottish texts.

Write the number of each question in the margin of your answer booklet and begin each essay on a fresh page.

You should spend about 45 minutes on each essay.

The following will be assessed:

- **the relevance of your essays to the questions you have chosen**

- **your knowledge and understanding of key elements, central concerns and significant details of the chosen texts**

- **your explanation of ways in which aspects of structure/style/language contribute to the meaning/effect/impact of the chosen texts**

- **your evaluation of the effectiveness of the chosen texts, supported by detailed and relevant evidence**

- **the quality and technical accuracy of your writing.**

Each question is worth 25 marks. The total for this paper is 50 marks.

SECTION A—DRAMA

Answers to questions in this section should refer to the text and to such relevant features as: characterisation, key scene(s), structure, climax, theme, plot, conflict, setting . . .

1. Choose a play in which a character loses the support of her/his friends or family during the course of the play.

   What reasons are there for this loss of support and what effect does this lack of support have on the character's fate in the play?

2. Choose a play which you feel has a memorable opening scene or section.

   Show how the content or atmosphere of the scene or section provides an effective starting point for the development of the characters and the theme of the play.

3. Choose a play in which a character hides the truth from other characters in the play.

   State what the character hides and show how the revealing of the truth affects the outcome of the play.

SECTION B—PROSE

Answers to questions in this section should refer to the text and to such relevant features as: characterisation, setting, language, key incident(s), climax/turning point, plot, structure, narrative technique, theme, ideas, description . . .

4. Choose a novel **or** short story which deals with an important human issue: for example, poverty, war, family conflict, injustice, or any other issue you regard as important.

   State what the issue is and show how the characters cope with the issue in the course of the novel or short story.

5. Choose a novel **or** short story in which the main character makes an important decision.

   Explain why a decision is necessary and go on to show how the decision affects the rest of the novel or short story.

6. Choose a non-fiction text or group of texts which presents you with an interesting place **or** topic.

   Briefly identify the place or topic and go on to show how the writer's presentation made this interesting to you.

SECTION C—POETRY

Answers to questions in this section should refer to the text and to such relevant features as: word choice, tone, imagery, structure, content, rhythm, theme, sound, ideas . . .

7. Choose a poem which deals with birth **or** death **or** love **or** hate **or** jealousy.

   By looking at the content and language of the poem show how your understanding of one of these topics is deepened by your reading of the poem.

8. Choose a poem which deals with nature or the natural world.

   State what aspect of nature is being described and show how the use of poetic techniques deepens your understanding and appreciation of the topic.

9. Choose a poem which arouses strong emotion in you.

   State what it is about the subject of the poem which makes you feel strongly, and go on to show how the poet's use of language reinforces these feelings.

[Turn over

SECTION D—FILM AND TV DRAMA

Answers to questions in this section should refer to the text and to such relevant features as: use of camera, key sequence, characterisation, mise-en-scène, editing, setting, music/sound effects, plot, dialogue . . .

10. Choose a film which has a child or young person as its main character.

    Show how the character is introduced in the film in such a way that you realise he/she is important.

11. Choose a film or TV drama* which raises awareness of an important social issue.

    Identify the issue and show how its importance is brought home to you through the characters who convey these ideas to you.

12. Choose a film or TV drama* which involves conflict between two groups of people.

    Explain the reasons for the conflict and show how the portrayal of the conflict is highlighted by the use of media techniques.

    * "TV drama" includes a single play, a series or a serial.

SECTION E—LANGUAGE

Answers to questions in this section should refer to the text and to such relevant features as: register, accent, dialect, slang, jargon, vocabulary, tone, abbreviation . . .

13. Consider the use of persuasive language in the field of politics, **or** charitable campaigns, **or** commercial advertising.

    Show how the language tries to persuade you and discuss how successful it is in its aim.

14. Consider the differences in spoken language between two groups—for example, the inhabitants of different areas.

    Analyse the main differences between the ways of speaking of these groups and consider reasons for the differences.

15. Consider the special language associated with a particular job, hobby or sport.

    By giving examples show how the specialist language differs from non-specialist language and say what advantage is gained by the use of specialist language within the group which uses it.

[END OF QUESTION PAPER]

[BLANK PAGE]

X115/201

NATIONAL QUALIFICATIONS 2007	FRIDAY, 11 MAY 1.00 PM – 2.00 PM	**ENGLISH INTERMEDIATE 2** Close Reading

Answer all questions.

30 marks are allocated to this paper.

Read the passage carefully and then answer **all** the questions, **using your own words as far as possible**.

The questions will ask you to show that:

> you understand the main ideas and important details in the passage—in other words, **what** the writer has said (**Understanding—U**);

> you can identify, using appropriate terms, the techniques the writer has used to get across these ideas—in other words, **how** he has said it (**Analysis—A**);

> you can, using appropriate evidence, comment on how effective the writer has been—in other words, **how well** he has said it (**Evaluation—E**).

A code letter (U, A, E) is used alongside each question to identify its purpose for you. The number of marks attached to each question will give some indication of the length of answer required.

Come fly with me

In this passage, the writer reflects on his fascination with birds and flight.

I was going through Monken Hadley churchyard and there were lots (note scientific precision) of house martins whizzing round the church tower. House martins are dapper little chaps, navy blue with white, and they are one of the sights of the summer: doing things like whizzing round church steeples and catching flies in their beaks. Later in the
5 season the young ones take up whizzing themselves, trying to get the hang of this flying business. So I paused on my journey to spend a few moments gazing at the whirligig of martins. It was nothing special, nothing exceptional, and it was very good indeed. Note this: one of the greatest pleasures of birdwatching is the quiet enjoyment of the absolutely ordinary.

10 And then it happened. Bam!

Gone.

From the tail of my eye, I saw what I took to be a kestrel. I turned my head to watch it as it climbed, and I waited for it to go into its hover, according to time-honoured kestrel custom. But it did nothing of the kind. It turned itself into an anchor. Or a
15 thunderbolt.

No kestrel this: it crashed into the crowd of martins, and almost as swiftly vanished. I think it got one, but I can't swear to it, it was all so fast.

It was a hobby-hawk. Perhaps the most dashing falcon of them all: slim, elegant and deadly fast. Not rare as rare-bird-addicts reckon things: they come to Britain in
20 reasonable numbers every summer to breed. The sight of a hobby-hawk makes no headlines in the birdwatching world. It was just a wonderful and wholly unexpected sight of a wonderful and wholly unexpected bird. It was a moment of perfect drama.

Birdwatching is a state of being, not an activity. It doesn't depend on place, on equipment, on specific purpose, like, say, fishing. It is not a matter of organic
25 trainspotting; it is about life and it is about living. It is a matter of keeping the eyes and ears and mind open. It is not a matter of obsession, not at all. It is just quiet enjoyment.

Flight is the dream of every human being. When we are lucky, we do, quite literally, dream about flying. They are the best of all dreams—you are free, you are miraculous.

The desire to fly is part of the condition of being human. That's why most of the
30 non-confrontational sports are about flying, or at least the defiance of gravity. Gymnastics is about the power of the human body to fly unaided; so is the high jump and the long jump. The throwing events—discus, shot-put and hammer—are about making something else fly: a war on gravity.

Golf always seems to me a trivial game, but every one of its legion of addicts will tell you
35 that it all comes back to the pure joy of a clean strike at the ball: making it defy gravity. Making it climb like a towering snipe. Making it soar like an eagle, at least in the mind of the striker, as it reaches the top of its long, graceful parabola.

Think about it: all these sports are done for the joy of flying. Skating is a victory over friction, and it feels like victory over gravity; it feels like flying. Its antithesis is
40 weightlifting: a huge and brutal event, the idea of which is to beat gravity. All the horsey events come back to the idea of flight: of getting off the ground, of escaping human limitations by joining up with another species and finding flight. For every rider, every horse has wings.

And birds fly in all kinds of ways: the brisk purpose of a sparrow, the airy detachment
45 of the seagull, the dramatic power of the hawk. Some birds specialise in flying very fast;
others in flying very slow. Great hunters such as the barn owl work on the edge of the
stall all the time. Kestrels are very good at flying without moving at all. Some birds are
not so great at flying. Pheasants just about get off the ground into a safe place in a tree
for a night. They are poor flyers, but they are unquestionably better than us humans.

50 And flight attracts our eyes, lifts our heart with joy and envy. Flight, to us earthbound
creatures, is a form of magic—one of the great powers attributed to decent wizards and
witches throughout history is the ability to fly, from the persecuted sorcerers of the Dark
Ages to the players of the game of quidditch.

Take a basic urban moment—a traffic jam, a train becalmed. A sigh, a look away from
55 the road or the newspaper, out of the window. A skein of geese in the sky; probably,
almost certainly, "just" Canada geese. Too far away to hear them honking to each other,
urgent instructions to keep the formation tight and to help the leader out with the hard
work. A daily sight, a common sight, an ordinary sight. But just for one
second—perhaps even two—you are let off the day's hassles. At least that is the case if
60 you take the trouble to look up. It will probably be the most inspiring thing you will see
all day. The day is the better for those birds.

And so we look to birds for a deep-seated kind of joy. It goes back to the dawn of
humankind: ever since humans first walked upright, they were able to turn their eyes to
the heavens and observe the birds. The birds have something we can never have. But
65 merely by existing—by flying before us—they add to the daily joys of existence. Birds
are about hope.

Adapted from *How to be a Bad Birdwatcher* by Simon Barnes

QUESTIONS   *Marks Code*

1. Explain what is odd or ironic about the expression "note scientific precision" (lines 1–2).   **2 A**

2. "It was nothing special, nothing exceptional, and it was very good indeed." (line 7).

   (*a*) What is surprising about this statement?   **1 A**

   (*b*) Show how the writer continues this idea in the next sentence (lines 8–9).   **2 U/A**

3. Identify **two** techniques used in lines 10 and 11 which help to convey the idea of speed described in the next two paragraphs (lines 12–17).   **2 A**

4. (*a*) What is the author suggesting about the bird when he says "It turned itself into an anchor" (line 14)?   **1 U/A**

   (*b*) Why is the comparison of the bird to a "thunderbolt" (line 15) an effective image or metaphor?   **2 E**

5. Explain with clear reference to the whole sentence why the writer uses a colon in line 19.   **2 A**

6. "The sight of a hobby-hawk makes no headlines in the birdwatching world" (lines 20–21). Explain **in your own words** what is meant by "makes no headlines".   **1 U**

7. Write down the word from later in the paragraph which continues the idea introduced by "trainspotting" (line 25).   **1 U**

8. In what way does the author's use of "quite literally" (line 27) help to make his meaning clear?   **1 U/A**

9. (*a*) What does "trivial" (line 34) tell us about the writer's attitude to golf?   **1 U**

   (*b*) Explain how an expression later in this sentence makes it clear that the author is aware that others do not share his opinion.   **2 U/A**

   (*c*) Why are the comparisons the writer uses in the rest of this paragraph appropriate?   **2 A/E**

10. The writer mentions a variety of sports between lines 29 and 43. What challenge does he think these activities have in common?   **1 U**

11. The writer refers to equestrianism ("horsey events", line 41), as related to the pursuit of flight. What is the difference between this and all the other sports he mentions? Answer **in your own words**.   **1 U**

12. Why is it appropriate to introduce the paragraph consisting of lines 44 to 49 with the expression "And birds fly in all kinds of ways"?   **2 A/E**

13. The writer refers to "wizards and witches throughout history" (lines 51–52). Explain by referring to either **word choice** or **structure** how the rest of the sentence continues this idea.   **2 U/A**

14. What do the writer's examples of "a basic urban moment" (line 54) have in common?   **1 U**

15. What is the effect of the inverted commas round "just" in line 56?   **1 A**

16. Explain fully why the last paragraph (lines 62–66) provides an appropriate or effective conclusion to the passage.   **2 E**

[END OF QUESTION PAPER]   **Total (30)**

X115/202

NATIONAL
QUALIFICATIONS
2007

FRIDAY, 11 MAY
2.20 PM – 3.50 PM

ENGLISH
INTERMEDIATE 2
Critical Essay

Answer **two** questions.

Each question must be taken from a different section.

Each question is worth 25 marks.

SCOTTISH
QUALIFICATIONS
AUTHORITY

Answer TWO questions from this paper.

Each question must be chosen from a different Section (A–E). You are not allowed to choose two questions from the same Section.

In all Sections you may use Scottish texts.

Write the number of each question in the margin of your answer booklet and begin each essay on a fresh page.

You should spend about 45 minutes on each essay.

The following will be assessed:

- **the relevance of your essays to the questions you have chosen**

- **your knowledge and understanding of key elements, central concerns and significant details of the chosen texts**

- **your explanation of ways in which aspects of structure/style/language contribute to the meaning/effect/impact of the chosen texts**

- **your evaluation of the effectiveness of the chosen texts, supported by detailed and relevant evidence**

- **the quality and technical accuracy of your writing.**

Each question is worth 25 marks. The total for this paper is 50 marks.

SECTION A—DRAMA

Answers to questions in this section should refer to the text and to such relevant features as: characterisation, key scene(s), structure, climax, theme, plot, conflict, setting . . .

1. Choose a play which portrays a strong relationship between two of the main characters.

    Describe the nature of the relationship and explain how the relationship influences the fate of the two characters concerned.

2. Choose a play in which there is a highly emotional scene.

    Show how this scene increases your understanding of the characters involved and how it is important in the unfolding of the plot of the play.

3. Choose a play which has, as a central concern, an issue which is of importance in today's society.

    State what the issue is and show how the playwright's handling of the plot and characters increases your understanding of the issue.

SECTION B—PROSE

Answers to questions in this section should refer to the text and to such relevant features as: characterisation, setting, language, key incident(s), climax/turning point, plot, structure, narrative technique, theme, ideas, description . . .

4. Choose a novel **or** short story in which **two** of the main characters have a disagreement which is important to the outcome of the novel or short story.

   Identify the reasons for the disagreement and go on to show how the effects of the disagreement have an impact on the rest of the novel or short story.

5. Choose a prose text (fiction or non-fiction) in which a society **or** a person **or** a culture **or** a setting is effectively portrayed.

   Show how the writer's presentation of the subject makes an impact on you, and helps you to understand the subject in greater depth.

6. Choose a novel **or** short story which has a striking opening.

   Show how the opening is effective in introducing the character(s) **and/or** the atmosphere **and/or** the setting.

SECTION C—POETRY

Answers to questions in this section should refer to the text and to such relevant features as: word choice, tone, imagery, structure, content, rhythm, theme, sound, ideas . . .

7. Choose a poem which seems to be about an ordinary everyday experience but which actually makes a deeper comment about life.

   Explain what the poem is about and go on to show how the techniques used by the poet help to make the ideas memorable.

8. Choose a poem which creates pity or sympathy in you.

   Show how the feelings of pity or sympathy are brought into focus by the use of poetic techniques.

9. Choose a poem which describes a scene or incident vividly.

   Briefly state what is being described and then go on to show how the poetic techniques used make the description vivid.

[Turn over

SECTION D—FILM AND TV DRAMA

Answers to questions in this section should refer to the text and to such relevant features as: use of camera, key sequence, characterisation, mise-en-scène, editing, setting, music/sound effects, plot, dialogue . . .

10. Choose a film or TV drama* which creates suspense or tension either in a particular scene **or** throughout the whole film or TV drama.

    Show how the suspense or tension is created and how it affects your enjoyment of the film or TV drama* as a whole.

11. Choose a film or TV drama* which deals with crime **or** espionage **or** detection.

    Show how the film or TV drama* captures and holds your interest by its choice of content and use of media techniques.

12. Choose a film or TV drama* which depends to some extent on humour to make an impact.

    Briefly state what you consider to be the humorous aspects of the film or TV drama* and go on to show how the film or programme makers use various techniques to create the humour.

    * "TV drama" includes a single play, a series or a serial.

SECTION E—LANGUAGE

Answers to questions in this section should refer to the text and to such relevant features as: register, accent, dialect, slang, jargon, vocabulary, tone, abbreviation . . .

13. Consider the aspects of language which make advertising effective.

    Choose two advertisements which you feel vary in their effectiveness. By looking closely at each advertisement explain why you felt that one was more effective than the other.

14. Consider the language of two groups of people who are different in some significant way. For example, they may be from different generations or different places.

    By looking at examples of the language of each group, describe the differences between the two, and discuss the advantages **and/or** disadvantages which might arise from the different ways of using language.

15. Consider a modern means of communication such as e-mailing or text-messaging.

    By referring to specific examples show what are the advantages and disadvantages of the method of communication which you have chosen.

[END OF QUESTION PAPER]

[BLANK PAGE]

X115/201

NATIONAL
QUALIFICATIONS
2008

THURSDAY, 15 MAY
1.00 PM – 2.00 PM

ENGLISH
INTERMEDIATE 2
Close Reading

Answer all questions.

30 marks are allocated to this paper.

Read the passage carefully and then answer **all** the questions, **using your own words as far as possible**.

The questions will ask you to show that:

> you understand the main ideas and important details in the passage—in other words, **what** the writer has said (**Understanding—U**);

> you can identify, using appropriate terms, the techniques the writer has used to get across these ideas—in other words, **how** he has said it (**Analysis—A**);

> you can, using appropriate evidence, comment on how effective the writer has been—in other words, **how well** he has said it (**Evaluation—E**).

A code letter (U, A, E) is used alongside each question to identify its purpose for you. The number of marks attached to each question will give some indication of the length of answer required.

Afar, far away

Matthew Parris describes the harsh conditions of life in North Africa, and suggests what may be in store for the region and the nomadic (wandering) people who live there.

At the beginning of this month I was in a hellish yet beautiful place. I was making a programme for Radio 4 about one of the world's most ancient trade routes. Every year, since (we suppose) at least the time of the Ancient Greeks, hundreds of thousands of camels are led, strung together in trains, from the highlands of Ethiopia into the Danakil
5 depression: a descent into the desert of nearly 10,000 feet, a journey of about 100 miles. Here, by the edge of a blue-black and bitter salt lake, great floes of rock salt encrusting the mud are prised up, hacked into slabs and loaded on to the camels.

Then the camels and their drivers make the climb through dry mountains back into the highlands, where the slabs are bound with tape and distributed across the Horn of
10 Africa.   The camels drink only twice on their journey, walking often at night, and carrying with them straw to eat on the way back. Their drivers bring only dry bread, sugar and tea.

Travelling with the camel trains in mid-winter, when temperatures are bearable, I found the experience extraordinarily moving. But my thoughts went beyond the salt trade, and
15 were powerfully reinforced by the journey that followed it—to another desert, the Algerian Sahara.

These reflections were first prompted by a chance remark that could not have been more wrong. Our superb Ethiopian guide, Solomon Berhe, was sitting with me in a friendly but flyblown village of sticks, stones, cardboard and tin in Hamed Ela, 300ft below sea
20 level, in a hot wind, on a hot night. An infinity of stars blazed above. The mysterious lake was close, and when the wind changed you could smell the sulphur blowing from a range of bubbling vents of gas, salt and super-heated steam. On the horizon fumed the volcano, Hertale. With not a blade of grass in sight, and all around us a desert of black rocks, the Danakil is a kind of inferno. How the Afar people manage to live in
25 this place, and why they choose to, puzzles the rest of Ethiopia, as it does me.

"But," said Solomon, scratching one of the small fly-bites that were troubling all of us, "if we could return here in 50 years, this village would be different. There will be streets, electricity, and proper buildings. As Ethiopia modernises, places like this will be made more comfortable for people. Hamed Ela will probably be a big town."

30 And that is where Solomon was wrong. As Ethiopia modernises, the Afar will leave their desert home. They will drift into the towns and cities in the highlands. Their voracious herds of goats will die. Their camels will no longer be of any use. The only remembrance this place will have of the humans it bred will be the stone fittings of their flimsy, ruined stick huts, and the mysterious black rock burial mounds that litter the
35 landscape.

There is no modern reason for human beings to live in such places. Their produce is pitiful, the climate brutal and the distances immense. Salt is already produced as cheaply by industrial means. If market forces don't kill the trade, the conscience of the animal rights movement will, for the laden camels suffer horribly on their journey. The
40 day is coming when camels will go down there no more. In fifty years the Danakil will be a national park, visited by rubbernecking tourists in helicopters. Camels will be found in zoos. Goats will be on their way to elimination from every ecologically fragile part of the planet.

Even in America, deserts are not properly inhabited any more. Unreal places such as
45 Las Vegas have sprung up where people live in an air-conditioned and artificially
irrigated bubble, but the land itself is emptier than before. Tribes who were part of the
land, and lived off it, have mostly gone, their descendants living in reservations. The
wilderness places of North America are vast and exceptionally well preserved; but they
are not part of many people's lives, except those of tourists. We are becoming outsiders
50 to the natural world, watching it on the Discovery Channel.

Those who call themselves environmentalists celebrate this. "Leave nothing and take
nothing away," read the signs at the gates of nature reserves. Practical advice, perhaps,
but is there not something melancholy in what that says about modern man's desired
relationship with nature? Will we one day confine ourselves to watching large parts of
55 our planet only from observation towers?

I have no argument against the international development movement that wants to see
the Afars in clean houses with running water and electrical power, and schools, and a
clinic nearby—away, in other words, from their gruesome desert life. All this is
inevitable.

60 But as that new way of living arrives—as we retreat from the wild places, and the fences
of national parks go up; as we cease the exploitation of animals, and the cow, the camel,
the sheep, the chicken and the pig become items in modern exhibition farms, where
schoolchildren see how mankind used to live; as our direct contact with our fellow
creatures is restricted to zoos, pets and fish tanks; and as every area of natural beauty is
65 set about with preservation orders and rules to keep human interference to a
minimum—will we not be separating ourselves from our planet in order, as we suppose,
to look after it better? Will we not be loving nature, but leaving it?

They say there is less traffic across the Sahara today than at any time in human history,
even if you include motor transport. The great days of camel caravans are over. As for
70 the inhabitants, the nomads are on a path to extinction as a culture. Nomadic life does
not fit the pattern of nation states, taxes, frontiers and controls. And though for them
there is now government encouragement to stay, their culture is doomed. Amid the
indescribable majesty of this place—the crumbling towers of black rock, the scream of
the jackal, the waterless canyons, yellow dunes, grey plateaus and purple thorn
75 bushes—I have felt like a visitor to a monumental ruin, walked by ghosts. There are
fragments of pottery, thousands of cave paintings of deer, giraffe, elephant, and men in
feathers, dancing . . . but no people, not a soul.

In the beginning, man is expelled from the Garden of Eden. In the end, perhaps, we
shall leave it of our own accord, closing the gate behind us.

From *The Times*, February 25, 2006 (slightly adapted)

QUESTIONS

Marks Code

1. What is surprising about the writer's **word choice** in the first sentence?   **2 A**

2. Why does the writer add the expression "we suppose" (line 3) to the sentence here?   **1 U**

3. The word "floes" (line 6) usually refers to icebergs.

    Explain how it is appropriate to use it as a metaphor to refer to the appearance of the rock salt deposits.   **2 A/E**

4. Explain how any **one** example of the writer's choice of descriptive detail in lines 10–12 emphasises the hardships of the journey.   **1 A**

5. Explain **in your own words** the contrasting impressions the writer has of the village in Hamed Ela (see lines 18–19).   **2 U**

6. Explain what the word "fumed" (line 22) suggests about the volcano, apart from having smoke coming from it.   **1 U**

7. Explain why the sentence "And that is where Solomon was wrong" (line 30) is an effective link between the paragraphs contained in lines 26 to 35.   **2 E**

8. What does the word "drift" suggest about how "the Afar will leave their desert home" (lines 30 –31)?   **1 U**

9. The writer tells us "There is no modern reason for human beings to live in such places" (line 36).

    Explain **in your own words two** reasons why this is the case.

    Look in the next three sentences (lines 36–39) for your answer.   **2 U**

10. Explain fully the appropriateness of the **word choice** of "rubbernecking tourists in helicopters" (line 41).   **2 A**

11. Explain how the writer develops the idea of Las Vegas being "Unreal" (line 44).   **2 A**

12. Explain why the expression "watching it on the Discovery Channel" (line 50) effectively illustrates our relationship with "wilderness places".   **2 E**

13. What is the effect of the writer's inclusion of the words "Those who call themselves" in the sentence beginning in line 51?   **1 U**

14. What is the **tone** of the two sentences in lines 52–55?   **1 A**

15. Explain how other words in lines 56–58 help us to work out the meaning or sense of "gruesome desert life".   **2 U**

16. Look at lines 60–67.

    (*a*) Identify any feature of **sentence structure** the writer uses effectively in this paragraph.   **1 A**

    (*b*) Show how your chosen feature helps to clarify or support the writer's argument.   **2 A**

17. Explain **in your own words** why "the nomads are on a path to extinction as a culture" (line 70).   **1 U**

18. Explain any reason why the final paragraph (lines 78–79) works well as a conclusion to the passage.   **2 E**

Total (30)

[END OF QUESTION PAPER]

X115/202

NATIONAL
QUALIFICATIONS
2008

THURSDAY, 15 MAY
2.20 PM – 3.50 PM

ENGLISH
INTERMEDIATE 2
Critical Essay

Answer **two** questions.

Each question must be taken from a different section.

Each question is worth 25 marks.

Answer TWO questions from this paper.

Each question must be chosen from a different Section (A–E). You are not allowed to choose two questions from the same Section.

In all Sections you may use Scottish texts.

Write the number of each question in the margin of your answer booklet and begin each essay on a fresh page.

You should spend about 45 minutes on each essay.

The following will be assessed:

- **the relevance of your essays to the questions you have chosen**

- **your knowledge and understanding of key elements, central concerns and significant details of the chosen texts**

- **your explanation of ways in which aspects of structure/style/language contribute to the meaning/effect/impact of the chosen texts**

- **your evaluation of the effectiveness of the chosen texts, supported by detailed and relevant evidence**

- **the quality and technical accuracy of your writing.**

Each question is worth 25 marks. The total for this paper is 50 marks.

SECTION A—DRAMA

Answers to questions in this section should refer to the text and to such relevant features as: characterisation, key scene(s), structure, climax, theme, plot, conflict, setting . . .

1. Choose a play in which there is a significant conflict between two characters.

   Describe the conflict and show how it is important to the development of the characterisation and theme of the play.

2. Choose a play which has a tragic ending.

   Show how the ending of the play results from the strengths and/or weaknesses of the main character(s).

3. Choose a play in which a character encounters difficulties within the community in which he or she lives.

   Show how the character copes with the difficulties he or she encounters and how his or her actions contribute to the theme of the play.

SECTION B—PROSE

Answers to questions in this section should refer to the text and to such relevant features as: characterisation, setting, language, key incident(s), climax/turning point, plot, structure, narrative technique, theme, ideas, description . . .

4. Choose a novel **or** short story which has a turning point or moment of realisation for at least one of the characters.

   Briefly describe what has led up to the turning point or moment. Go on to show what impact this has on the character(s) and how it affects the outcome of the novel or story.

5. Choose a novel **or** short story in which you feel sympathy with one of the main characters because of the difficulties or injustice or hardships she or he has to face.

   Describe the problems the character faces and show by what means you are made to feel sympathy for her or him.

6. Choose a non-fiction text **or** group of texts which uses setting, **or** humour, **or** description to make clear to you an interesting aspect of a society.

   Show how the use of any of these techniques helped you to understand the writer's point of view on the interesting aspect of this society.

SECTION C—POETRY

Answers to questions in this section should refer to the text and to such relevant features as: word choice, tone, imagery, structure, content, rhythm, theme, sound, ideas . . .

7. Choose a poem which creates an atmosphere of sadness, pity, or loss.

   Show how the poet creates the atmosphere and what effect it has on your response to the subject matter of the poem.

8. Choose a poem about a strong relationship—for example, between two people, or between a person and a place.

   Show how the poet, by the choice of content and the skilful use of techniques, helps you to appreciate the strength of the relationship.

9. Choose a poem which reflects on an aspect of human behaviour in such a way as to deepen your understanding of human nature.

   Describe the aspect of human behaviour which you have identified and show how the poet's use of ideas and techniques brought you to a deeper understanding of human nature.

[Turn over

SECTION D—FILM AND TV DRAMA

Answers to questions in this section should refer to the text and to such relevant features as: use of camera, key sequence, characterisation, mise-en-scène, editing, setting, music/sound effects, plot, dialogue . . .

10. Choose a film or TV drama* which involves the pursuit of power or the fulfilment of an ambition.

    Show how the theme is developed through the presentation of character and setting.

11. Choose an opening sequence from a film which effectively holds your interest and makes you want to watch the rest of the film.

    Show what elements of the opening sequence have this effect, and how they relate to the film as a whole.

12. Choose a film or TV drama* which reflects an important aspect of society.

    Describe the aspect of society being dealt with and show how the techniques used by the film or programme maker help to deepen your understanding of the importance of this aspect.

* "TV drama" includes a single play, a series or a serial.

SECTION E—LANGUAGE

Answers to questions in this section should refer to the text and to such relevant features as: register, accent, dialect, slang, jargon, vocabulary, tone, abbreviation . . .

13. Consider the language of advertising.

    In any one advertisement identify the ways in which language is used successfully. Explain what it is about these usages which makes them effective.

14. Consider the language of any form of modern electronic communication.

    Identify some features of this language which differ from normal usage and say how effective you think these features are in communicating information.

15. Consider the distinctive language of any specific group of people.

    What aspects of the group's language are distinctive and what advantage does the group gain from the use of such language?

[END OF QUESTION PAPER]

[BLANK PAGE]

X115/201

NATIONAL
QUALIFICATIONS
2009

FRIDAY, 15 MAY
1.00 PM – 2.00 PM

ENGLISH
INTERMEDIATE 2
Close Reading

Answer all questions.

30 marks are allocated to this paper.

Read the passage carefully and then answer **all** the questions, **using your own words as far as possible**.

The questions will ask you to show that:

> you understand the main ideas and important details in the passage—in other words, **what** the writer has said (**Understanding—U**);

> you can identify, using appropriate terms, the techniques the writer has used to get across these ideas—in other words, **how** he has said it (**Analysis—A**);

> you can, using appropriate evidence, comment on how effective the writer has been—in other words, **how well** he has said it (**Evaluation—E**).

A code letter (U, A, E) is used alongside each question to identify its purpose for you. The number of marks attached to each question will give some indication of the length of answer required.

©

Why Dickens was the hero of Soweto

In this passage, the writer informs us about the effect that books by Charles Dickens, a 19th-century English writer, had on black South African children during the time of racial segregation ("apartheid") in South Africa. "Afrikaans" was the form of Dutch spoken in South Africa by some white rulers before the arrival of democracy in that country.

Hector Pieterson was 12 when he died. Today a museum bearing his name commemorates his death—and hundreds of others—which occurred some 30 years ago at a place whose name has come to symbolise uprising against oppression: Soweto.

Hector was one of thousands of black children who took to the streets on June 16, 1976,
5 in protest about schooling under the apartheid regime in South Africa. When police opened fire on the march it brought the word Soweto to the attention of the world. But less well known is the role that Charles Dickens played in events.

The march was in protest at a government edict making Afrikaans compulsory in schools. From January 1976, half of all subjects were to be taught in it, including ones in
10 which difficulties of translation were often an issue.

To pupils accustomed to being educated in English, the Afrikaans policy was the last of a line of insults delivered in the name of "Bantu" or "native education". They thought being taught in Afrikaans, the language of a regime that had tried to "unpeople" them, would cost them their last remaining freedom—that of thinking for themselves, using
15 their minds.

That is where Dickens came in. Many books were banned under apartheid but not the classics of English literature. Pupils arriving hungry at school every day were captivated by the story of a frail but courageous boy named Oliver Twist.

The book was a revelation. Systemised oppression of children happened in England too!
20 They were not alone. Slave labour, thin rations and cruel taunts were part of a child's life in the world outside as well.

One former pupil, now in his forties, says of Dickens: "Four or five of us would be together and discuss the stories. And to think he wasn't banned! The authorities didn't know what was in these books, how they helped us to be strong, to think that we were
25 not forgotten."

Not being forgotten was particularly crucial. The apartheid regime had tried to "vanish" black people. Feeling abandoned and isolated, people turned to Dickens as someone who understood their plight.

But there were not enough books to go round. Few of the crateloads of Shakespeare,
30 Hardy and Dickens shipped from Britain reached the townships. Instead, they came to Soweto in parcels from charities. They were read by candlelight, often out loud, shared in a circle, or passed from hand to hand.

At Morris Isaacson School, one of the moving forces behind the Soweto protest, which produced two of its leaders, Murphy Morobe, "Shakespeare's best friend in Africa", and
35 Tsietsi Mashinini, there were 1,500 pupils and three copies of *Oliver Twist* in 1976. The former pupils recall waiting months for their turn, with a similar wait for *Nicholas Nickleby*.

But it was Oliver that they took to heart: students at one of the country's leading black colleges, Lovedale, formed a committee to ask for more.

40 Calling it the Board, after Dickens's Board of Guardians, they asked for more lessons, more food—and more and better books. Their reward was to be charged with public violence. All 152 "board" members were expelled from the college and some were jailed.

They felt that Dickens was obviously on their side. Descriptions of Gamfield's "ugly leer" and Bumble's "repulsive countenance" and Oliver being beaten by Mrs
45 Sowerberry and shoved "but nothing daunted" into the dust-cellar were evidence that this English author understood the plight of black South Africans.

Dickens's compassion for the poor linked the people of Soweto to a worldwide literature of tremendous importance.

The veteran South African trumpeter Hugh Masekela later chose *Nicholas Nickleby* as
50 his favourite book on a popular radio programme, *Desert Island Discs*, telling the presenter what its author did for people in the townships: "He taught us suffering is the same everywhere."

The love of books that enabled an author dead for more than 100 years to inspire thousands of schoolchildren came mainly from grandmothers who had educated their
55 families orally, then urged them to read widely and learn all that they could.

It also came from people such as the activist Steve Biko, whose own mentor, the Brazilian educator Paulo Freire, spent a lifetime working with forest people who had no formal education, teaching them to "name the world their own way".

That is what the youth of Soweto wanted—a future in their own words. And they got it.

60 "Africans are not dustbins," declared some of the June 16 placards; and "Beware of Afrikaans, the most dangerous drug for our future." By the following year, the language had been withdrawn from classrooms as unworkable. And so, thanks to the influence of a long-dead British author, the sacrifices of Hector Pieterson and many other Africans have proved to be not entirely in vain —which Dickens himself would surely applaud.

Adapted from an article by Carol Lee in *The Times*, 10th June, 2006

QUESTIONS   *Marks Code*

1. Explain fully any way in which the writer makes the opening paragraph dramatic.   **2 A**

2. The writer tells us that Soweto "has come to symbolise uprising against oppression" (line 3).

   Write down one expression from the next paragraph (lines 4–7) which continues the idea of uprising, **and** one which continues the idea of oppression.   **2 U**

3. Explain **in your own words**

   (*a*) what the marchers were objecting to, according to lines 8–10;   **2 U**

   (*b*) why this issue was so important to them, according to lines 11–15.   **1 U**

4. Look at lines 16–25.

   (*a*) Explain **in your own words** why Dickens's books were not "banned under apartheid" (line 16).   **1 U**

   (*b*) **In your own words** explain why Dickens's book *Oliver Twist* would have "captivated" the Soweto children.   **2 U**

5. Explain the purpose of the exclamation mark in line 23.   **1 A**

6. "But there were not enough books to go round." (line 29)

   (*a*) Explain how this sentence provides a link between paragraphs at this point.   **2 A**

   (*b*) Explain fully how the paragraph between lines 33 and 37 illustrates the idea that there were not enough books to go round.   **2 A**

7. Explain why the writer's use of "reward" in line 41 is ironic.   **2 A**

8. Explain why the writer's use of examples from the writing of Dickens in lines 43 to 46 is effective in advancing her argument at this point.   **3 E**

9. Look at lines 49–52.

   Explain **in your own words** why Hugh Masekela thought Dickens was so important.   **2 U**

10. Explain **in your own words** how the grandmothers referred to in line 54 instilled a love of books in their grandchildren.   **2 U**

11. Explain how any aspect of the **structure** of the paragraph in line 59 contributes to its effectiveness.   **2 A**

12. Look at the placard text "Beware of Afrikaans, the most dangerous drug for our future". (lines 60–61)

    Explain why this expression is an effective image or metaphor.   **2 A/E**

13. Look at the last paragraph of the passage (lines 60–64).

    Explain fully why this provides an effective conclusion to the passage.   **2 A/E**

                                                                                                    Total (30)

[END OF QUESTION PAPER]

X115/202

NATIONAL
QUALIFICATIONS
2009

FRIDAY, 15 MAY
2.20 PM – 3.50 PM

ENGLISH
INTERMEDIATE 2
Critical Essay

Answer **two** questions.

Each question must be taken from a different section.

Each question is worth 25 marks.

Answer TWO questions from this paper.

Each question must be chosen from a different Section (A–E). You are not allowed to choose two questions from the same Section.

In all Sections you may use Scottish texts.

Write the number of each question in the margin of your answer booklet and begin each essay on a fresh page.

You should spend about 45 minutes on each essay.

The following will be assessed:

- **the relevance of your essays to the questions you have chosen**

- **your knowledge and understanding of key elements, central concerns and significant details of the chosen texts**

- **your explanation of ways in which aspects of structure/style/language contribute to the meaning/effect/impact of the chosen texts**

- **your evaluation of the effectiveness of the chosen texts, supported by detailed and relevant evidence**

- **the quality and technical accuracy of your writing.**

Each question is worth 25 marks. The total for this paper is 50 marks.

SECTION A—DRAMA

Answers to questions in this section should refer to the text and to such relevant features as: characterisation, key scene(s), structure, climax, theme, plot, conflict, setting . . .

1. Choose a character from a play whose fate is unfortunate or unhappy.

   Show how much of the character's misfortune is caused by the personality and decisions of the character and how much by other circumstances in the play.

2. Choose a scene from a play in which suspense or tension is built up.

   Show how this suspense or tension is built up and what effect this scene has on the play as a whole.

3. Choose a play which deals with a close relationship within a family or a community.

   Show how the portrayal of the relationship helps in your understanding of the central concerns of the play.

SECTION B—PROSE

Answers to questions in this section should refer to the text and to such relevant features as: characterisation, setting, language, key incident(s), climax/turning point, plot, structure, narrative technique, theme, ideas, description . . .

4. Choose a novel **or** a short story in which a character is in conflict with his or her friends or relatives or society.

   Show how the conflict arises and what effect it has on the character's fate in the novel or short story as a whole.

5. Choose a novel **or** a short story which deals with the effects of evil or war or deceit or a breakdown in society or a breakdown in relationship(s).

   Show how any of these negative pressures affects the main character in the novel or short story and go on to show whether or not she or he tackles it successfully.

6. Choose a **non-fiction** text **or** group of texts which interests you because of its detailed and vivid description of scenes, events, people.

   Show how the detailed description makes the scenes, events, people vivid for you and increases your understanding of what is happening.

SECTION C—POETRY

Answers to questions in this section should refer to the text and to such relevant features as: word choice, tone, imagery, structure, content, rhythm, theme, sound, ideas . . .

7. Choose a poem which deals with childhood, adolescence, family life or old age.

   Show how the poet deepens your understanding of any of these stages of life by the choice of content and the skilful use of poetic techniques.

8. Choose a poem which deals with a particular time of year or a particular place.

   Show how the poet, by his or her choice of content and style, persuades you to adopt his or her view of the season or the place.

9. Choose a poem which has as one of its central concerns a personal, social or religious issue.

   Show how the content and the poetic techniques used increase your understanding of the issue.

[Turn over

SECTION D—FILM AND TV DRAMA

Answers to questions in this section should refer to the text and to such relevant features as: use of camera, key sequence, characterisation, mise-en-scène, editing, setting, music/sound effects, plot, dialogue . . .

10. Choose a film **or** TV drama* which both entertains and helps to raise awareness of social issues.

    Show how the film or TV drama you have chosen succeeds in both these aspects.

11. Choose a sequence from a film which is important both to the atmosphere and to the plot of the film.

    Show how atmosphere is created in the sequence and go on to show how the sequence and the atmosphere are important to the film as a whole.

12. Choose a film **or** TV drama* which is set **either** in a past age **or** in the future.

    Show how the director/programme-maker has created the setting of the past **or** the future and go on to show how the setting increases your enjoyment of the film or TV drama.

    * "TV drama" includes a single play, a series or a serial.

SECTION E—LANGUAGE

Answers to questions in this section should refer to the text and to such relevant features as: register, accent, dialect, slang, jargon, vocabulary, tone, abbreviation . . .

13. Consider how TV programmes aimed at young audiences have an effect on the language young people use.

    Identify any recent changes in vocabulary or accent that you are aware of and explain whether you feel the new words/accents are more effective in communicating than those which they have replaced.

14. Consider the use of emotive language in any form of advertising with which you are familiar.

    By referring to specific examples show how effective you feel the use of emotive language is in its particular context.

15. Consider the distinctive language found in any group of people with a shared interest in a sport, hobby, job or activity.

    By referring to specific examples of distinctive vocabulary or codes or grammatical forms show whether or not these features increase the effectiveness of communication within the group.

[END OF QUESTION PAPER]

2010

[BLANK PAGE]

X115/201

NATIONAL
QUALIFICATIONS
2010

THURSDAY, 13 MAY
1.00 PM – 2.00 PM

ENGLISH
INTERMEDIATE 2
Close Reading

Answer all questions.

30 marks are allocated to this paper.

Read the passage carefully and then answer **all** the questions, **using your own words as far as possible**.

The questions will ask you to show that:

you understand the main ideas and important details in the passage—in other words, **what** the writer has said (**Understanding—U**);

you can identify, using appropriate terms, the techniques the writer has used to get across these ideas—in other words, **how** he has said it (**Analysis—A**);

you can, using appropriate evidence, comment on how effective the writer has been—in other words, **how well** he has said it (**Evaluation—E**).

A code letter (U, A, E) is used alongside each question to identify its purpose for you. The number of marks attached to each question will give some indication of the length of answer required.

The Mighty Qin

This piece was written round about the time that an exhibition of some of the warriors from the ancient Chinese Terracotta Army was on display in the British Museum in London.

Qin Shi Who? My reaction entirely. I had heard of the Terracotta Army, of course. I had even seen some of them when a vanguard of warriors came to London in the 1980s. But I couldn't have told you who Qin Shihuangdi (pronounced *Chin Shur Hwang Dee*) was. Even if you'd said he was the First Emperor of China, I'd have had only the haziest
5 recollection of what you were talking about.

That probably goes for the vast majority of people in the West. And given that he is one of the most colossal figures ever to have walked the earth, that is rather shocking. For Qin Shihuangdi, its First Emperor, created China more than two millennia ago, establishing the world's longest-lasting empire. A visionary, a brutal tyrant and a
10 megalomaniac, he is the greatest historical figure that most of us have never heard of.

I only began to grasp this a few months ago when I travelled to Xi'an to visit the First Emperor's mind-boggling mausoleum, home to his Terracotta Army. "This is one of the people who changed the world," said Neil MacGregor, director of the British Museum. "There are terribly few historical figures whose achievements lasted like that.
15 This is really one of the great, great figures in human history."

The written historical sources for the man who bequeathed his name to his country are scant. Born Ying Zheng in 259 BC, he was the son of the king of Qin, in central China. He succeeded at the age of 13 and there was a period when he ruled with a regent. Then, when he was properly established on the throne, he embarked on what was
20 China's only real revolution until the 20th century.

Through clever diplomacy and brilliant military strategy he conquered and subdued neighbouring states. He achieved this by developing a highly organised army. Qin chariots had an improved design of smaller wheels with more spokes that provided greater stability and durability. The width of axles was made uniform, a seemingly small
25 innovation with massive repercussions: the chariots could ride relatively smoothly down the same ruts in the road and so avoid churning up the entire highway. The light infantry were armed with extremely sharp bronze weapons and crossbows and supported by cavalry.

This formidable war machine brought the warring states under the control of Qin, and
30 the heart of the area that we now call China was united for the first time in 221 BC. Ying Zheng decided to mark the success by renaming himself Qin Shihuangdi, or First Emperor of Qin.

The first Emperor survived at least three assassination attempts in subsequent years, incidents that served to tighten his grip on every aspect of life. He created a surveillance
35 culture in which neighbours were expected to spy on each other and lived in fear of terrible punishments for failing to do so or for breaking the many laws. One of the most miserable punishments, which very often proved to be a death sentence, was to be dispatched into the wilderness to toil on the construction of the wall Qin Shihuangdi had ordered to be built along the northern frontier of the empire.

40 Although there had been a tradition of building walls to mark the boundaries of territory and keep neighbours out, the First Emperor's undertaking was the most significant building project to date, aiming to protect the borders from nomads. His wall was rather farther north than what we think of today as the Great Wall, which is the series of fortifications (not one single wall) built in the Ming Dynasty, which ruled China for

45 almost three centuries from 1368. Little of the Qin wall remains beyond a few mounds
that are believed to be from the First Emperor's era. But he is regarded as the
grandfather of the Great Wall, that iconic symbol of China's historical separateness and
age-old industriousness.

The First Emperor's imprint on the lives of the inhabitants of his far-flung kingdoms
50 was seen further. He unified the script, demanding that all states write the pictographs
of ancient Chinese in the same way. So, although the words might be pronounced
differently in different parts of the empire, once they were written down everyone who
could read could understand each other, a particular advantage for traders. Some of the
pictographs are recognisable in the language today, and the principle of a single written
55 language that can be spoken in different ways remains.

But for the First Emperor, establishing complete control over his empire was not
enough. He wanted to rule forever. If he couldn't have immortality in this world, the
next best thing would be to rule in the nether world. We knew about his tomb mound
because the ancient sources referred to it, and it has always been there.

60 The tomb itself may never be opened because of the sensitivities of disturbing the
Emperor, although some archaeologists hope that improved technology may one day
allow some form of exploration.

The ancient sources refer to 700,000 people labouring on the tomb, but make no
reference to what else the Emperor had devised under the ground. This is presumably
65 because they didn't know about his subterranean empire, which lay undisturbed until
1974. Those of the 600 pits that have been examined have yielded almost 1,800 mass-
produced clay figures with another 6,000 believed to exist. In this mountain fastness
Qin Shihuangdi wanted an army to protect him from his enemies, but also wanted his
civil servants on hand and musicians and acrobats to entertain him.

70 "I can't think of anyone else who had the scale of ambition to think of replicating their
entire kingdom," says MacGregor. "Nobody else in human history has attempted to do
that, and what is fascinating is that it's the eternal underground that has survived and
nothing else. We have no buildings, we have no writings, this is all that survives. The
people making the figures knew they were making them to serve the Emperor and live
75 forever. And in a funny way they have."

The Emperor went to his tomb rather earlier than he had intended. In 210 BC, on one
of his imperial progresses, he fell ill and died in his carriage.

There is no substitute for seeing the mass ranks of the Terracotta Army. But the British
Museum wants to do two things: show visitors a selection of warriors up close in a way
80 that is not possible in Xi'an, and tell the story of the man whose breathtaking
megalomania gave us one of the wonders of the world. The telling of that story is long
overdue.

Damian Whitworth in *The Times*

QUESTIONS

Marks Code

1. Looking in the opening paragraph (lines 1–5) for your answer, explain **in your own words** what the writer's original "reaction" to the name Qin Shihuangdi was.

1 U

2. The first paragraph (lines 1–5) is written in a chatty style. Identify **one** expression or feature from these lines which contributes to this chattiness, and explain why it does so.

2 A

3. Look at paragraph 2 (lines 6–10).

   Give **in your own words two** reasons why it is "rather shocking" that most people in the West do not know about Qin.

2 U

4. Show how any **one** feature of Neil MacGregor's word choice (see lines 12–15) makes it clear that he thinks of Qin as someone special.

2 A

5. Explain **in your own words two** of the consequences of the improvements Qin made to his war chariots (see lines 24–26).

2 U

6. How appropriate is the expression "formidable war machine" (line 29) at this point in the passage?

3 E

7. Explain **in your own words** any **two** ways in which Qin managed to "tighten his grip on every aspect of life" (line 34).

2 U

8. What does the writer gain by using "toil" (line 38) rather than the word "work"?

1 A

9. The writer calls the Great Wall an "iconic symbol" (line 47).

   (*a*) Why is it appropriate to call the wall a "symbol"?

1 A/E

   (*b*) **In your own words**, explain fully what aspects of China it symbolises.

3 U

10. Explain how the sentence "But for the First Emperor, establishing complete control over his empire was not enough." (lines 56–57) works as a link between paragraphs at this point.

2 A

11. Show fully how the writer introduces a **tone** of doubt when he writes about the prospects for opening the tomb (lines 60–62).

2 A

12. How does the writer convey the grandness or large scale of the tomb in lines 63–69? You should refer to technique as well as content.

2 A

13. Show how an aspect of what Neil MacGregor says (lines 70–75) effectively conveys his sense of wonder.

    Your answer should refer to an example of **word choice or structure**.

2 E

14. In what sense does the writer use "funny" in line 75?

1 U

15. Explain why any example of the **word choice** in the final paragraph (lines 78–82) contributes to a neat conclusion to the passage.

2 A

Total (30)

[END OF QUESTION PAPER]

X115/202

NATIONAL
QUALIFICATIONS
2010

THURSDAY, 13 MAY
2.20 PM – 3.50 PM

ENGLISH
INTERMEDIATE 2
Critical Essay

Answer **two** questions.

Each question must be taken from a different section.

Each question is worth 25 marks.

Answer TWO questions from this paper.

Each question must be chosen from a different Section (A–E). You are not allowed to choose two questions from the same Section.

In all Sections you may use Scottish texts.

Write the number of each question in the margin of your answer booklet and begin each essay on a fresh page.

You should spend about 45 minutes on each essay.

The following will be assessed:

- the relevance of your essays to the questions you have chosen

- your knowledge and understanding of key elements, central concerns and significant details of the chosen texts

- your explanation of ways in which aspects of structure/style/language contribute to the meaning/effect/impact of the chosen texts

- your evaluation of the effectiveness of the chosen texts, supported by detailed and relevant evidence

- the quality and technical accuracy of your writing.

Each question is worth 25 marks. The total for this paper is 50 marks.

SECTION A—DRAMA

Answers to questions in this section should refer to the text and to such relevant features as: characterisation, key scene(s), structure, climax, theme, plot, conflict, setting . . .

1. Choose a play in which a central character feels increasingly isolated from those around her or him.

   Explain why the character finds herself or himself isolated, and show what the consequences are for the character concerned.

2. Choose a scene from a play in which there is an important incident which leads to a turning point in the action.

   Explain what happens in the scene, and then go on to say how it affects the outcome of the play.

3. Choose a play in which one of the main concerns is love **or** jealousy **or** betrayal **or** reconciliation.

   Explain what the concern is, and show how it is explored throughout the play.

SECTION B—PROSE

Answers to questions in this section should refer to the text and to such relevant features as: characterisation, setting, language, key incident(s), climax, turning point, plot, structure, narrative technique, theme, ideas, description . . .

4. Choose a novel **or** a short story which gives you an insight into an aspect of human nature or behaviour.

   State what the aspect is, and show how the characters' actions and relationships lead you to a deeper understanding of human nature or behaviour.

5. Choose a novel **or** a short story with an ending which you find satisfactory.

   By looking at the novel or short story as a whole, explain why you find the ending satisfactory in bringing to a conclusion the main concerns of the text.

6. Choose a prose work (fiction **or** non-fiction) in which setting is an important feature.

   Explain how the writer creates the setting, and then go on to show how this feature contributes to your understanding of the text as a whole.

SECTION C—POETRY

Answers to questions in this section should refer to the text and to such relevant features as: word choice, tone, imagery, structure, content, rhythm, theme, sound, ideas . . .

7. Choose a poem which could be considered as having a powerful message.

   Show how the poet effectively conveys this message through his or her use of poetic techniques.

8. Choose a poem in which the poet creates a particular mood or atmosphere.

   Show how the poet creates this mood or atmosphere by his or her choice of subject matter and use of poetic techniques.

9. Choose a poem which portrays an interesting character.

   Show how the poet uses poetic techniques to make the character interesting.

[Turn over

SECTION D—FILM AND TV DRAMA

Answers to questions in this section should refer to the text and to such relevant features as: use of camera, key sequence, characterisation, mise-en-scène, editing, setting, music/sound, special effects, plot, dialogue . . .

10. Choose a film **or** TV drama* which deals with issues which mainly affect young people.

    Explain how the film or TV drama* deals with such issues, stating whether or not you find the portrayal of these issues realistic.

11. Choose a scene or sequence from a film or TV drama* which provides a climax to the action.

    Briefly describe the events leading up to the climax, and then explain how the techniques used by the film or programme makers create a heightened sense of importance in this scene or sequence.

12. Choose a film which you think is typical of its genre, for example: action, romance, comedy, horror . . .

    Explain how the film makers have used the features of the genre to create a successful film.

* "TV drama" includes a single play, a series or a serial.

SECTION E—LANGUAGE

Answers to questions in this section should refer to the text and to such relevant features as: register, accent, dialect, slang, jargon, vocabulary, tone, abbreviation . . .

13. Consider a text which you find to be persuasive, for example: an advertisement, a speech, a newspaper article . . .

    By referring to specific examples from your chosen text, show how persuasive techniques have been used to convince you.

14. Consider the ways that young people use the internet to communicate and socialise, for example: networking sites, instant messaging, chat rooms, blogs . . .

    By referring to specific examples of language and vocabulary, explain how such communication differs from formal English, and what its attractions are for young people.

15. Consider the specialist language used by any group which has a common leisure, vocational or geographical connection.

    Show how the specialist language used by the group is effective in communicating shared interests accurately.

[END OF QUESTION PAPER]

[BLANK PAGE]

[BLANK PAGE]

[BLANK PAGE]

Acknowledgements

Permission has been sought from all relevant copyright holders and Bright Red Publishing is grateful for the use of the following:

The article 'Women and Chocolate: Simply made for each other' by Glenda Cooper © The Times/NI Syndication, 14 March 2004 (2006 Close Reading pages 2–3);

An extract from 'How to be a Bad Birdwatcher' by Simon Barnes. Published by Short Books Ltd. (2007 Close Reading pages 2–3);

The article 'We are outsiders to the natural world, preferring to watch it on Discovery' taken from The Times, 25 February 2006. Reproduced by permission of Matthew Parris (2008 Close Reading pages 2–3);

An extract from 'A Child Called Freedom' by Carol Lee, published by Century 2006. Reprinted by permission of The Random House Group Ltd. (2009 Close Reading pages 2–3).

The article 'The Mighty Qin' by Damian Whitworth taken from The Times © The Times/NI Syndication August 30th 2007 (2010 Close Reading pages 2–3).